For anyone who carries a little piece of St Andrews in their heart.

Published by Cartographie Press Ltd.
Designed and Set by Cartographie Press Ltd.
www.cartographie.co.uk

I Love ST ANDREWS

CARLY BROWN & GILLIAN GAMBLE

In Fife there is an old grey town
that stands beside the wide North Sea.
Of all the places in the world,
this town is where I love to be.

It's home to scholars and a saint
and sometimes even future kings,

although it is just a wee place,
this town has seen a lot of things.

I saw it first in summertime.
We went there on a holiday.
With picnic baskets in our arms
we ran down to the beach to play.

On West Sands, we built sandcastles
and flew our brightly coloured kites.
We watched the dogs dash through the surf
and children riding past on bikes.

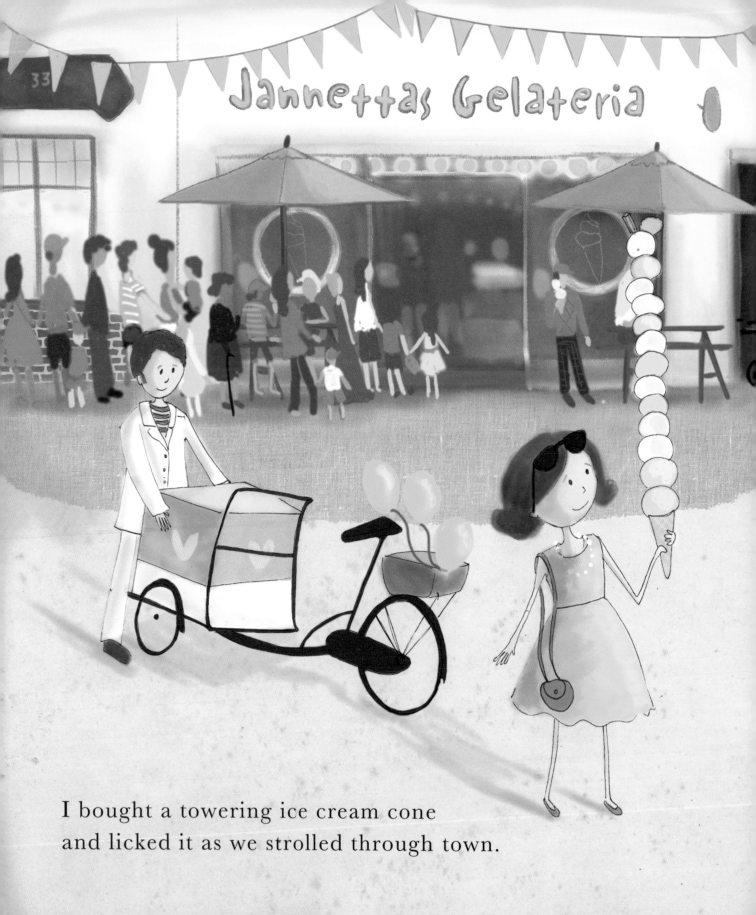

I bought a towering ice cream cone
and licked it as we strolled through town.

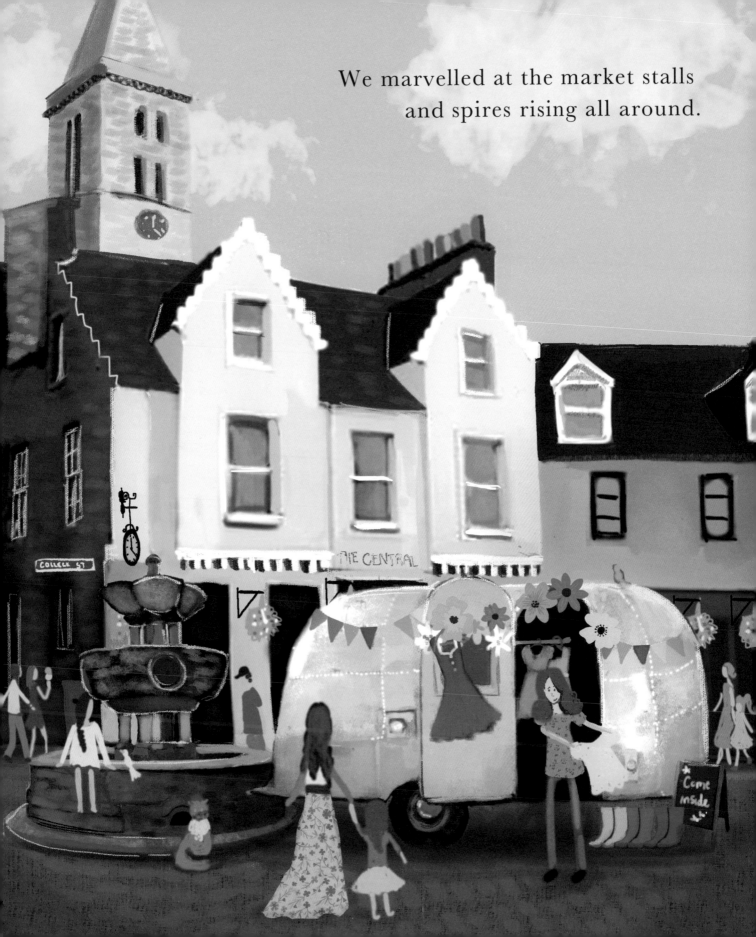

We marvelled at the market stalls
and spires rising all around.

They took me to a windy green
with waving grass and tiny flags.

We had a go at hitting balls
with silver poles from canvas bags.

I learned this was where golf was born,
back in the fifteenth century.
I didn't know how long that was
(it seemed a while ago to me).

I saw some people wearing robes,
bright apple red and flapping free.
My mother said: 'They're special gowns
you wear for university.'

Then I walked down the long stone pier,
which reaches out into the sea,
and looking back at St Andrews,
thought: this is where I want to be.

St Andrews.
CIRCUS
1966

A few years later, I came back
to study in that little town.

I couldn't wait to make new friends
and get to wear a bright red gown.

I met people from Canada
and India and Scotland too.
My new friends came from near and far
to study here in St Andrews.

There were so many things to learn
about the town and our degrees,

a famous place we could not step
and 'academic families'.

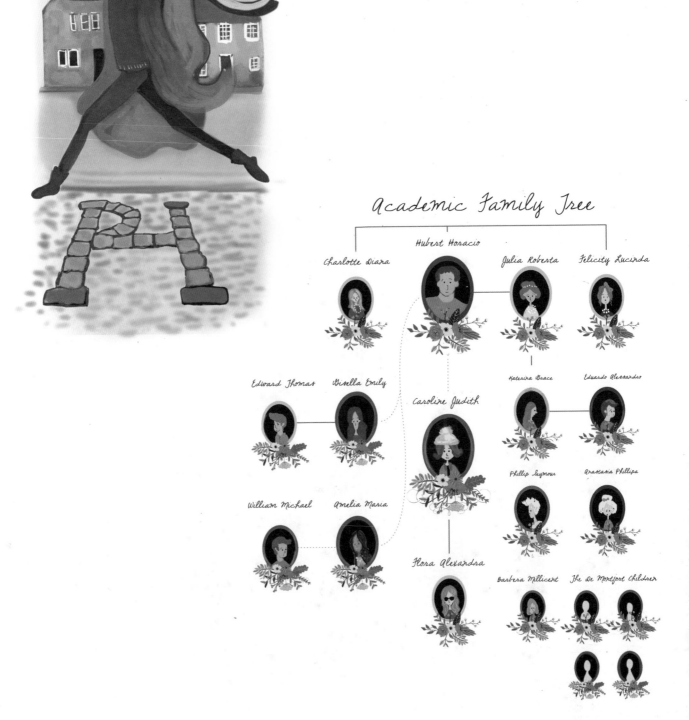

Academic Family Tree

Hubert Horacio

Charlotte Diana   Julia Roberta   Felicity Lucinda

Edward Thomas   Gisella Emily   Katerina Grace   Eduardo Alessandro

Caroline Judith

William Michael   Amelia Maria   Phillip Seymour   Anastasia Phillipa

Flora Alexandra

Barbera Millicent   The De Montfort Children

University Packing List

THERE'S NO SUCH THING AS BAD WEATHER IN ST ANDREWS— ONLY THE WRONG CLOTHES.

How to wear your academic gown

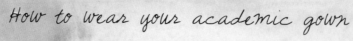

1ST YEAR   2ND YEAR   3RD YEAR   4TH YEAR   DIVINITY

The Stereoscope and Kaleidoscope, both invented by Sir David Brewster, Universirty Principal, 1838-1859

James Gregory 1638-1675

On Raisin Weekend, we stayed out
and celebrated through the night.
We put some crazy costumes on
and joined in for a big foam fight!

I learned about a ginger cat
beloved by everyone around,
and saw the new statue of him
built in the centre of the town.

This bold orange adventurer,
Hamish McHamish, ruled the street.
He made friends with the shopkeepers
and all the people he would meet.

We soon started to feel at home
when walking down through Lade Braes Park,
chatting beside the winding creek,
beneath the trees, 'til it got dark.

Hallow Hill

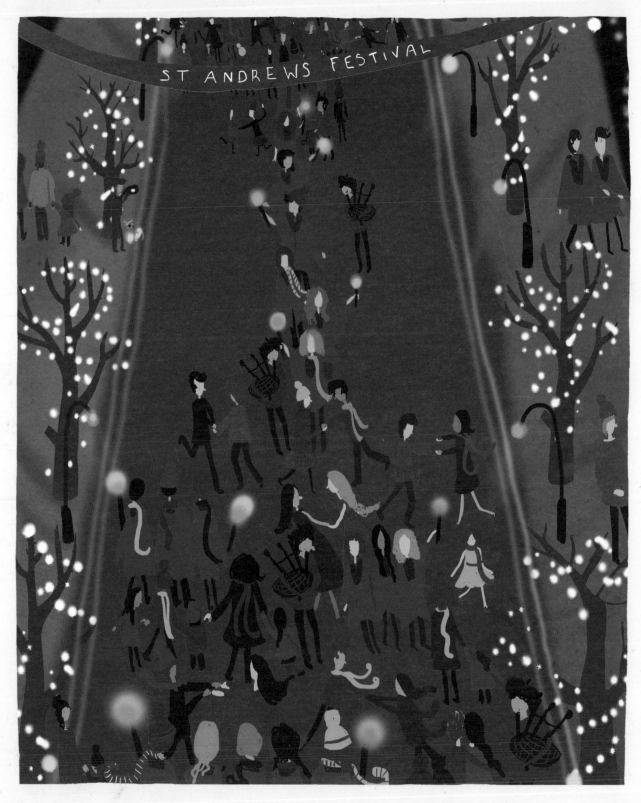

Then fairy lights began to glow
on lamp posts and on Christmas trees.

In knitted hats we bundled up
against the biting North Sea breeze.

In cafes, we sipped mugs of tea
and laughed until we fogged the glass.
Outside the windowpane we watched
friends passing on their way to class.

We heard music in favourite pubs
as candles flickered, calm and bright.
We sang along to fiddle songs
all through the chilly winter night.

It was the time for carols too,
at night at Holy Trinity.
We stood inside the cathedral;
our voices rose like smoke from tea.

But sometimes it was time to walk
across the ancient cobblestones,
to hear the echoes of the past
and feel as though you're not alone.

For on those long and windy nights,
and in that silent time of year,
when you would listen really close,
it's History's footsteps you could hear.

Down the ancient narrow wynd,
or there behind that big gravestone,
is that the ghost of old John Knox
or Walter Scott walking alone?

Then winter winds began to still
and fireworks bloomed in the sky.

We welcomed in the year to come
and waved the year before goodbye.

For auld lang syne, my jo,
For auld lang syne,
We'll tak a cup o' kindness yet,
For auld lang syne,

And in the gardens, snow bells bloomed,
beside the yellow daffodils,

and couples kissed by soft lamplight
across the town where Kate met Wills.

We watched processions in the streets
and listened to the pipers play,

as beaming brides in white lace gowns
took photos for their marriage day.

We saw glittering fashion shows
and dressed up for a springtime ball,

and spun and twirled to ceilidh tunes
while trying our best not to fall.

Then on the first of May we ran
into the North Sea holding hands,
and huddled by a big bonfire,
the sun rising on Castle Sands.

And looking out at all my friends
silhouetted by the sea,
I knew I loved the little town.
These people meant so much to me.

We donned our graduation robes
and posed for all the photographs.
We toasted to our favourite town
and ate desserts and had some laughs.

Then, walking down the old stone pier,
I looked back at the little town
there on the edge of the grey cliffs,
with white waves crashing all around.

So many stories in this place,
from this day back to ancient time.
I'm glad I was part of its tale
and that it was a part of mine.

Then stars appeared within the sky.
The North Sea shone under the moon.
I waved goodbye to St Andrews
and promised I would be back soon!

In Loving Memory of

Hamish
McHamish

I would like to thank three wonderful writers, Lydia Cruz, Laala Kashef Alghata and Rosie McCaffrey for helping me at various stages of the editorial process. I would also like to thank my mom for always encouraging me to follow my passions, even when that meant moving across an ocean. Finally, a big heartfelt thanks to the great friends I made in St Andrews, who were a constant source of inspiration, love and support.

-Carly

Thank you to everyone who made my life in St Andrews so special. To Jenny Stirling & Julia Ogilvy who both helped me in every imaginable way in life, to Professor Robert Crawford who opened my imagination in his classes and through his writing, to the support staff of the university and to the many wonderful friends from over the years who are just too numerous to mention. Thank you also to Maria Amelia Randall, for being a constant artistic colleague and a wonderful source of support and critique. St Andrews also gave me a darling husband Stephen and a beautiful wee girl Maria, and the town itself offered such a beautiful setting for love to grow. Thank you to my family for all of their encouragement, but particularly my grandparents Maureen and George for everything they do to make life that little bit brighter.

-Gillian